A11906 002600

DISCARD

# All About Phonics
# Consonants

by
Lillian Lieberman

Illustrated by
Marilynn G. Barr

Publisher: Roberta Suid
Production: Little Acorn & Associates, Inc.

Entire contents copyright © 2002 by Monday Morning Books, Inc.,

For a complete catalog, write to the address below
Monday Morning Books, Inc
PO Box 1134
Inverness, CA 94937

Call our toll-free number: 1-800-255-6049
E-mail us at: MMBooks@aol.com
Visit our Web site:
http://www.mondaymorningbooks.com

ISBN 1-57612-157-7

Printed in the United States of America
9 8 7 6 5 4 3 2 1

# Contents

Introduction ..................................................................... 4
Enrichment Activities ...................................................... 6
Bulletin Boards ................................................................ 7

**Initial Consonants**
Consonant Booklet ........................................................ 10
Initial Consonants f, g, h ................................................ 32
Initial Consonants b, c, m .............................................. 33
Initial Consonants v, t, w ............................................... 34
Initial Consonants d, s, y ................................................ 35
Initial Consonants j, l, p ................................................. 36
Initial Consonants n, q, r ............................................... 37
**Shopping Trip** (Initial Consonants Game) ..................... 38

**Final Consonants**
Final Consonants g, t, n ................................................. 42
Final Consonants b, m, s ................................................ 43
Final Consonants k, p, f ................................................. 44
Final Consonants d, r, l ,x .............................................. 45
**Chicks and Eggs** (Final Consonants Game) ................... 46
Initial and Final Consonants .......................................... 49
Words ........................................................................... 50
Sentences ..................................................................... 52

**Mini-Story Books**
The Bag ......................................................................... 54
Can Not ......................................................................... 56
Green Man ..................................................................... 58
Silly Duck ....................................................................... 60
The Mouse in the House ................................................. 62
Phonics Award ............................................................... 64

# Introduction

**All About Phonics: Consonants** is a book of worksheets and activities that introduces the consonant letters and sound to kindergarten through second-grade children. It covers both initial and final consonants. The simple and motivating activities presented in the book are easy and fun for the children. They involve a variety of hands-on activities such as cut-and-paste, matching, writing, games, and more. The activities foster the development of skills essential to beginning reading and writing.

The consonant sounds are first introduced by a cut-and-paste activity, matching pictures to the letter and sound for each consonant. The pages are designed to be assembled into a book to take home. A Letter to the Parents provides suggestions for consonant reinforcement at home. Draw-a-line and circling activities for mixed practice follow, giving the children a chance to discriminate between initial and final consonant picture matches. Write-ins ask the children to fill-in the missing initial or final consonant letters by tracing, naming, and sounding the letters. Entertaining and easy-to-make and play games reinforce the consonant sounds. Enrichment activities as well as bulletin board suggestions are included for active whole-class involvement.

The children will enjoy the delightful mini-story books at the end of the book. Picture support and predictable context will encourage the emergent reader. Children may take the books home to share with family and friends. An award at the end of the book celebrates the children's mastery of the consonants.

# How to Make and Use

**Consonants Take-Home Booklets**

**To Make:** Cut construction paper and fold to make booklet folders for <u>My Consonants Sound Book</u>. Provide a booklet cover page (page 10) for each child. Have each child write his/her name on the booklet cover and cut-and-paste the cover on the folded construction paper cover. Put pages 11-31 into the folder and staple on the left side. Write each child's name on the bottom right-hand corner of the booklet.

**To Use:** Have children take the booklet home with the Letter to Parents to share. Have the parents enrich and reinforce learning by following the suggestions given in the Letter to Parents.

**Bulletin Board, Enrichment, Games, Worksheet Activities:** Follow the directions given for each.

**Mini-Story Books:** Duplicate the mini-story books. Cut the pages apart and place in order. Staple on the left-hand side. To familiarize the children with the words in the story, write them on the board or a chart to study. A similar sentence as in the story can be written for the children to supply the words. Example: The ___ is in the ___. Words may be written on index cards and placed on the chalkboard railing to play simple games. Example: Remove a word card and have a child tell the missing word. Children may also trace the word with their fingers, name the letters and say the word. Sand-writing is another fun way to learn the words. Read the story with individual children or a small group. Have the children take their books home to share.

**Awards:** Duplicate an award (page 64) for each child. Have children write their names on their awards. The teacher signs the award. Children may color the picture. Congratulate the children for mastering their consonants and have them take their awards home to share.

Spider Web

# Enrichment Activities

**Egg-Carton Consonants:** (Initial Consonants)

**Materials:** egg cartons, construction paper, small items, cookie sheet or tray, felt pen

**To Make:** Cut egg cartons in half lengthwise. Cut small slips of construction paper and write a consonant at the top of each. Collect small articles that begin with the consonant sounds, such as a penny, ball, feather, and ring, and place them on a cookie sheet or tray.

**To Play:** 3 players may play. Give each child a half carton and six consonant slips. Have children place one consonant slip in each egg cup. Each child in turn tries to find an item on the tray or cookie sheet that matches their consonants. The first child to fill all 6 egg cups with consonant matches is the winner. This game can be played several times, giving players different consonants to play.

**Big-Foot Consonants:** (Initial or Final Consonants)

**Materials:** sturdy card stock paper or poster board, felt pen, masking tape (optional), list of words for either initial or final consonant sound

**To Make:** Cut out very large footprints from heavy card stock or poster board. Write a consonant letter on each with a felt pen. Place the footprints on the floor within easy jumping spaces. Tape the footprints to the floor if necessary.

**To Play:** Have each child in turn listen to a dictated word and identify the initial consonant sound and letter. Have the child jump to the footprint with that consonant letter. If the child makes it, he/she gets another turn. Limit jumps to three at the most. Give each child a chance to identify the consonants and jump. At another time, dictate words for final consonant identification and play in the same manner.

**Consonant Hunt:** (Initial or Final Consonants)

**Materials:** large sticky notes, felt pen

**To Make:** Write a consonant letter on each sticky note. Make one for each child. Duplicates are fine.

**To Play:** Give a sticky note consonant to each child. Have the children hunt for an object that matches by initial consonant sound. They stick their note onto the object. Each child shares their find by naming the object.

# Bulletin Board

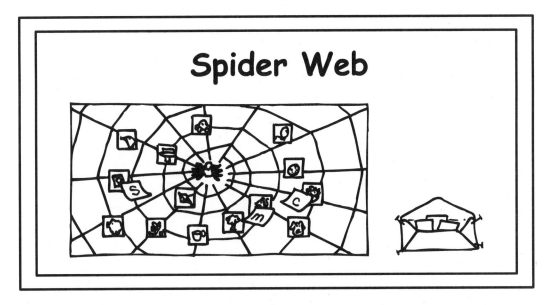

**Spider Web** (Initial or Final Consonants)

**Materials:** large sheet of oak tag, bulletin board pins, stapler, white index cards, large sticky notes, magazines or old workbooks, envelope or small box, felt pen, black pipe cleaners, bulletin board letters

**To Make:** With bulletin board letters, make the title of the bulletin board and pin to the top of the bulletin board. Draw a big spider web on a large sheet of oak tag. Staple the web under the title. Draw and cut out or make a fuzzy spider from black pipe cleaners. Pin it on the spider web. Cut 20 index cards to match the size of the sticky notes. Draw or cut and paste pictures from magazines or old workbooks that match initial consonants on the cards. Pin the cards on different parts of the web. On 20 large sticky notes, write in large print the letters of the consonants, one on each note. Place these in an envelope or box stapled to the bottom of the bulletin board.

**To Play:** 2 players may play. Each child takes a consonant note in turn and finds the consonant picture match on the web by initial sound. Players stick the consonant letter onto its matching picture. After play, children take off the sticky consonant notes and play again or give two other children their turn. Players may help each other find matches if necessary.

**Variation:** Make or find pictures that match final consonants. Write the final consonants on sticky notes. Children match consonants to pictures by final consonant sound. Word cards can be used in place of pictures for advanced players.

# Bulletin Board

**Consonant Mailbox** (Initial or Final Consonants)

**Materials:** large sheet of oak tag, construction paper, index cards, envelopes, felt pens, brass fasteners, stapler, large manila envelope, yarn, old workbooks or magazines, bulletin board pins, and letters

**To Make:** With bulletin board letters, make the title of the bulletin board and pin to the top of the bulletin board. Draw and cut out a large shape of a mailbox from oak tag. Color an index card red with a felt pen or cover with red construction paper to make the mail flag. Cut and glue an index card on the flag for a handle or pole. Attach to the mailbox with a brass fastener. Staple mailbox to the bulletin board. Write initial consonant letters on the backs of envelopes. Staple onto the mailbox with flaps open. Place the flag down until "mail" is in the mailbox. Cut a large manila envelope in half to make a mail bag. Cover with blue construction paper if desired. Label it "Mail," and staple to the bottom of the bulletin board, leaving the top open. Pin a yarn handle for the mail bag. Cut and paste initial consonant match pictures onto index cards and place in the mail bag.

**To Play:** 3 or more players may play. Children take picture cards in turn and place the cards in the matching consonant envelopes. When all the envelopes are filled, the red flag goes up. A child can be designated as "letter carrier" and removes the "mail." The red flag goes down until another set of cards has been placed in the envelopes.

**Variation:** Picture cards and envelopes for final consonants can be made. Children find picture-consonant matches for final consonants. Word cards can be used in place of picture cards for more advanced players.

# Letter to Parents

Dear Parents,

Your child is entering the exciting world of letters and sounds. Join in the fun by sharing in your child's first attempts with consonant letters and sounds. Have your child name and sound familiar objects in the home and attach sticky notes with matching letters or labels. Go on a hunt to gather small items that begin or end the same way. Make each day a Letter Day by selecting a letter for the day and hunting for items whose names begin or end with that letter. Read books or children's magazines together and have the child point out any letters or sounds he/she knows.

Go over your child's take home books and worksheets and reinforce the learning. Provide large crayons, pencils, and paper so your child can practice the consonant letters and even try to "spell" words.

Whatever you do, encourage your child and make learning consonant letters and sounds an enjoyable and pleasant experience.

Warmly,

_____

Teacher

# My Cut and Paste
# Consonant Sounds Book

_____

Name

Name _____

Cut and paste the pictures that begin with Bb as in <u>bag</u>.
Trace the Bb.

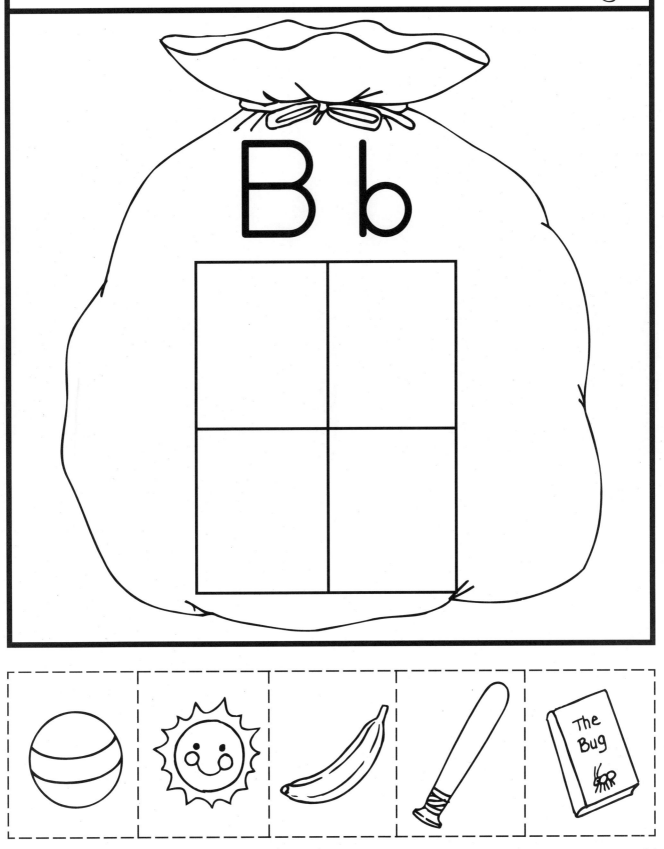

Name _____

Cut and paste the pictures that begin with Cc as in <u>cake</u>. 
Trace the Cc.

C c

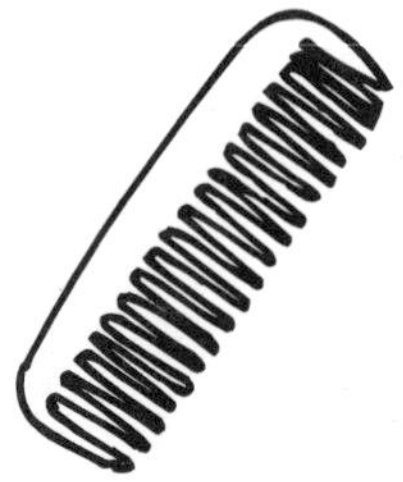

Name _____

Cut and paste the pictures that begin with Dd as in <u>duck</u>.
Trace the Dd.

# D d

Name _____

Cut and paste the pictures that begin with Ff as in <u>frog</u>.
Trace the Ff.

F f

Consonants © 2002 Monday Morning Books, Inc.

Name _____

Cut and paste the pictures that begin with Gg as in <u>ghost</u>.
Trace the Gg.

Name _____

Cut and paste the pictures that begin with Hh as in <u>house</u>.
Trace the Hh.

Name _____

Cut and paste the pictures that begin with Jj as in
jack-o'-lantern. Trace the Jj.

Name _____

Cut and paste the pictures that begin with Kk as in <u>kite</u>.
Trace the Kk.

K k

Name _____

Cut and paste the pictures that begin with Ll as in <u>lion</u>.
Trace the Ll.

Name _____

Cut and paste the pictures that begin with Mm as in
<u>moon</u>. Trace the Mm.

Name _____

Cut and paste the pictures that begin with Nn as in <u>net</u>.
Trace the Nn.

Consonants © 2002 Monday Morning Books, Inc.

Name _____

Cut and paste the pictures that begin with Pp as in <u>pig</u>.
Trace the Pp.

Name _____

Cut and paste the pictures that begin with Qq as in
<u>quilt</u>. Trace the Qq .

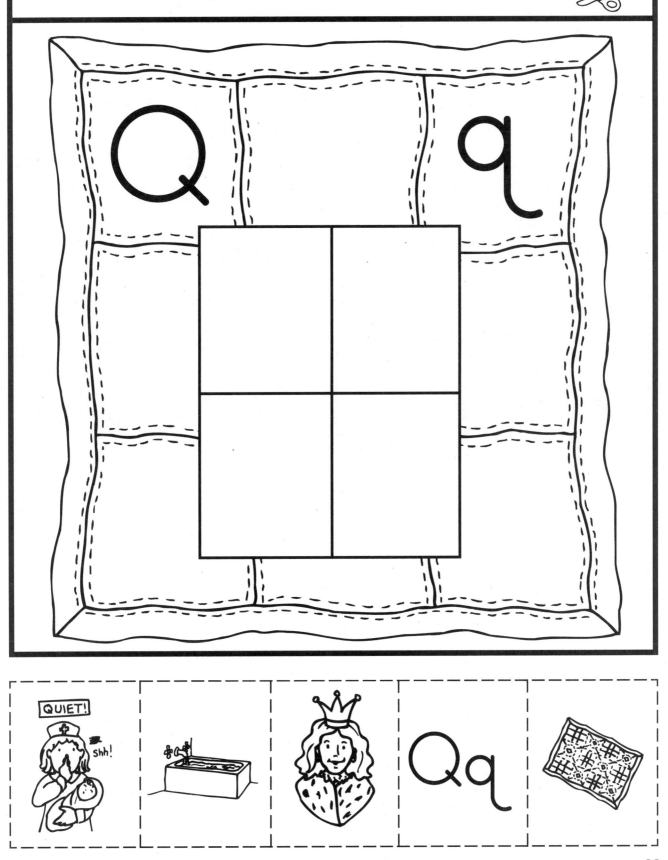

Name _____

Cut and paste the pictures that begin with Rr as in <u>robot</u>.
Trace the Rr.

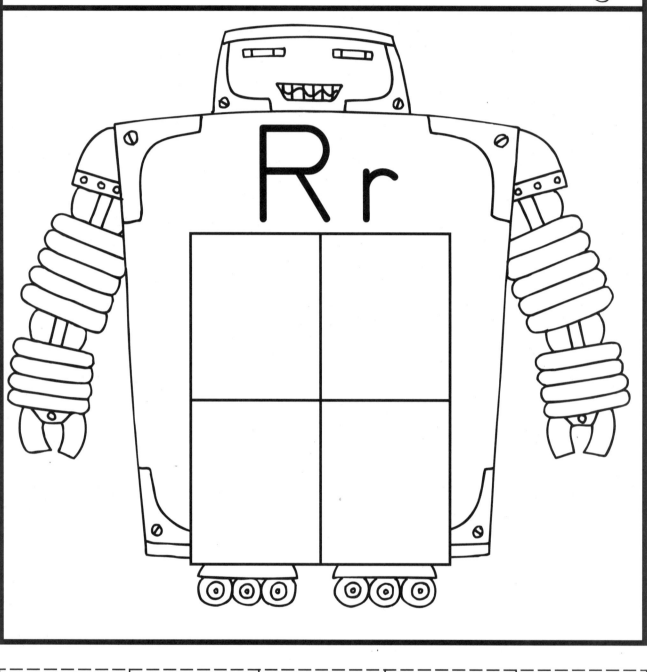

Name _____

Cut and paste the pictures that begin with Ss as in <u>sun</u>.
Trace the Ss.

Name _____

Cut and paste the pictures that begin with Tt as in <u>tent</u>.
Trace the Tt.

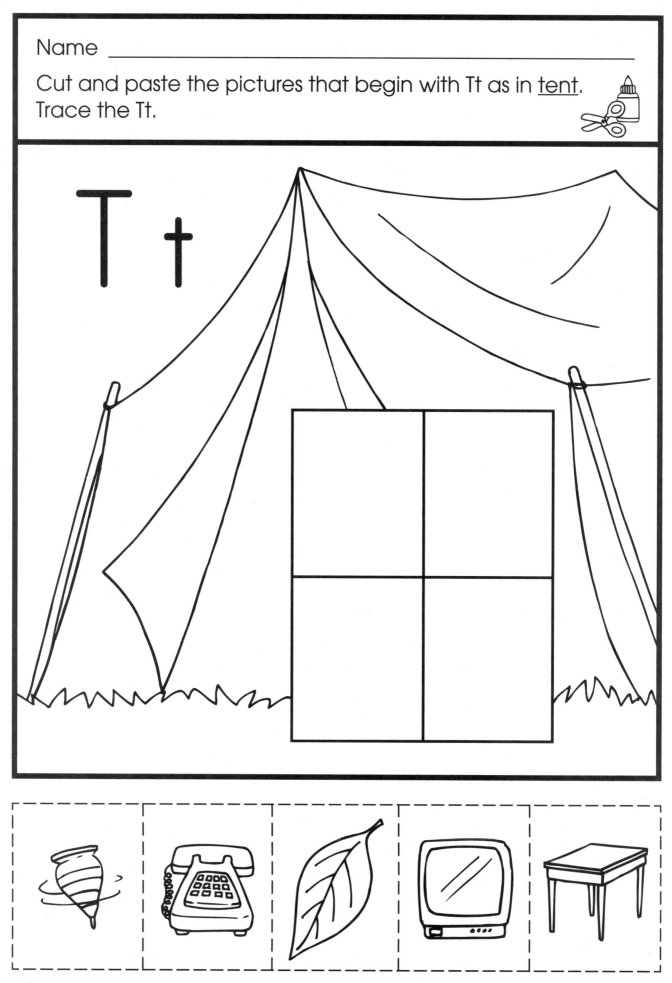

T t

Name _____

Cut and paste the pictures that begin with Vv as in <u>van</u>.
Trace the Vv.

6

Name _____

Cut and paste the pictures that begin with Ww as in <u>wagon</u>. Trace the Ww.

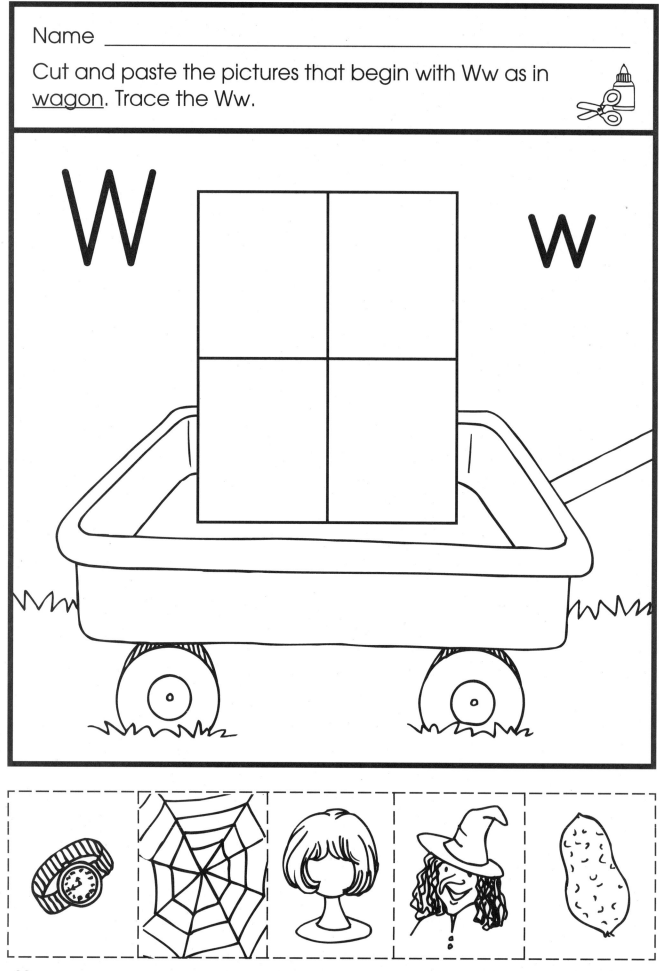

Name _____

Cut and paste the pictures that end with Xx as in bo<u>x</u>.
Trace the Xx.

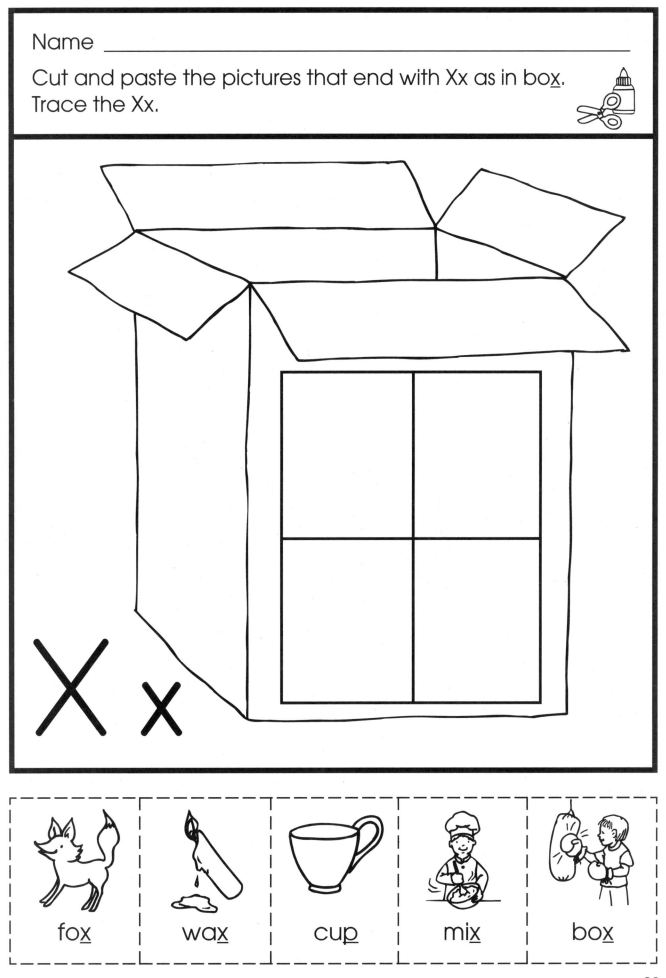

fo<u>x</u>    wa<u>x</u>    cu<u>p</u>    mi<u>x</u>    bo<u>x</u>

Name _____

Cut and paste the pictures that begin with Yy as in <u>yarn</u>.
Trace the Yy .

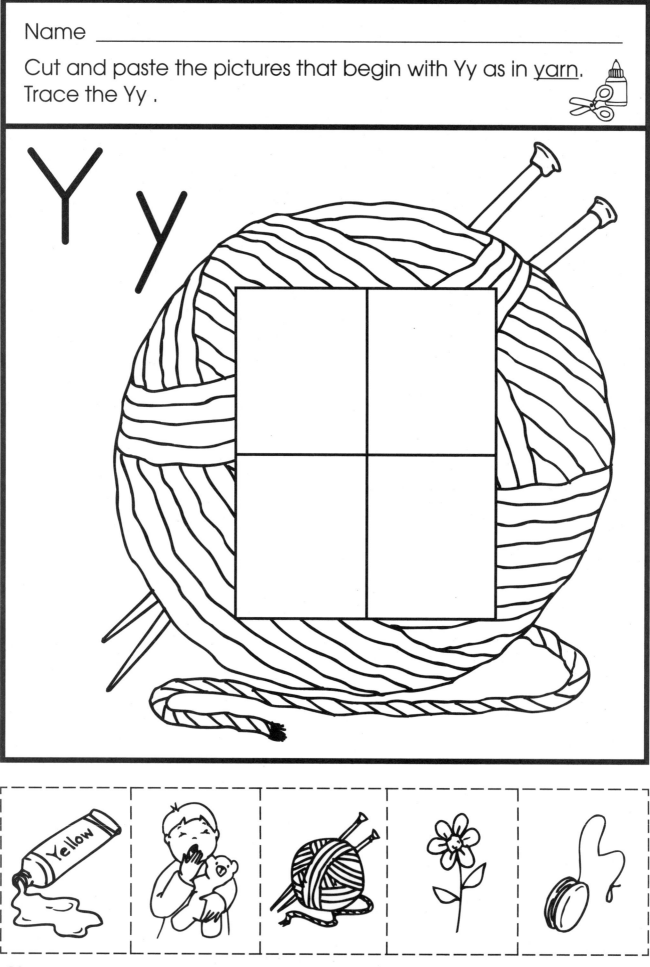

Consonants © 2002 Monday Morning Books, Inc.

Name _____

Cut and paste the pictures that begin with Zz as in <u>zebra</u>.
Trace the Zz.

Z z

Trace the letters. Name the picture. Write the letter for the first sound for each picture.

f  g  h

___ as

___ it

___ ug

___ ig

___ ish

___ um

Trace the letters. Name the picture. Write the letter for the first sound for each picture.

b    c    m

___ug

___an

___ut

___an

___ask

___un

Trace the letters. Name the picture. Write the letter for the first sound for each picture.

V    t    W

___et

___ag

10 ___en

___et

___ell

___an

Trace the letters. Name the picture. Write the letter for the first sound for each picture.

d    s    y

___og

___o‾yo

___ad

___esk

___arn

___ix

Trace the letters. Name the picture. Write the letter for the first sound for each picture.

j      l      p

___ug

___amp

___in

___et

___ips

___en

Trace the letters. Name the picture. Write the letter for the first sound for each picture.

n   q   r

_____ueen

_____ock

_____ut

_____uilt

_____at

_____est

# Shopping Trip

## Shopping Trip
### Initial Consonants

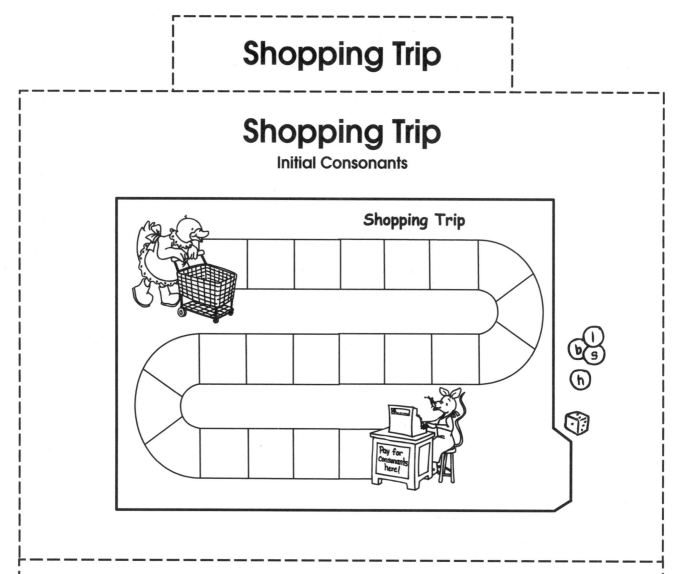

**How to Play:** (For 3 children)

Set out the board game in the playing area with markers and consonant circles. Place the consonant circles on the game spaces. Each player takes a marker and places it on the shopping cart. Provide a die. Have each player in turn throw the die and move their marker that number of spaces. Player names the consonant on the space landed on. To take the consonant, player must name a word that begins with the consonant sound. If player cannot name a word, player may not take a consonant. If player lands on an empty space, player remains there until the next turn. Play ends when the first player reaches the end. Player with the most consonants wins. The game may be played several times for a Super Winner!

**How to Make:**

Duplicate the game pages. Trim and glue the board set-up and glue inside a file folder. Glue the consonant letter circles page onto oak tag. Cut out the consonant letter circles and three markers. Provide a die. Glue a clasp manila envelope to the back of the file folder. Enclose the letter circles, markers, and die in the clasp envelope. Cut out and glue the game title onto the file folder tab. Cut out the **How to Play** directions and glue on the front of the file folder.

# Shopping Trip

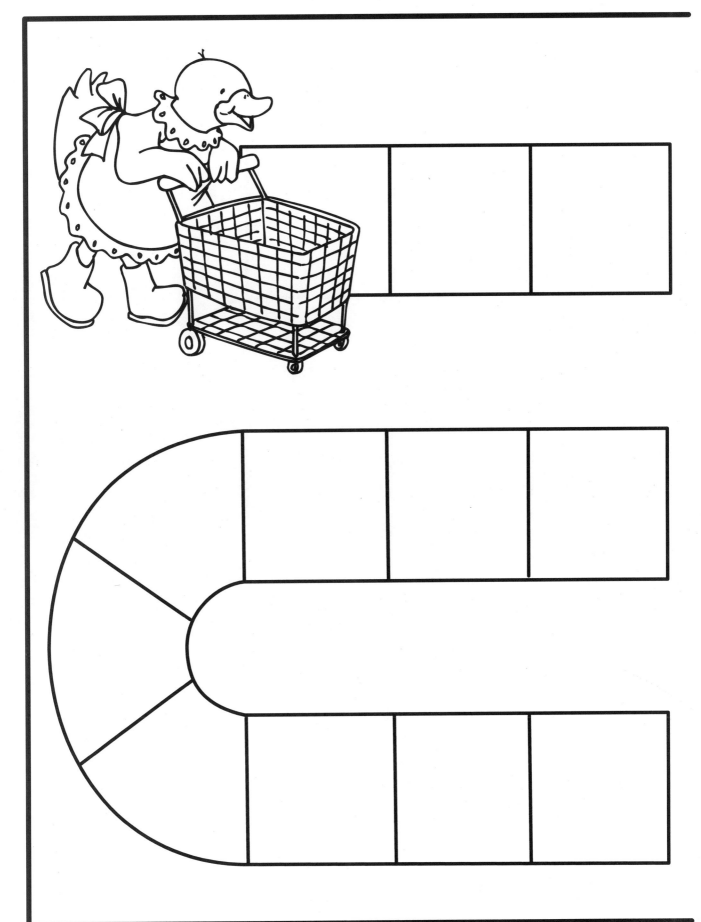

# Shopping Trip

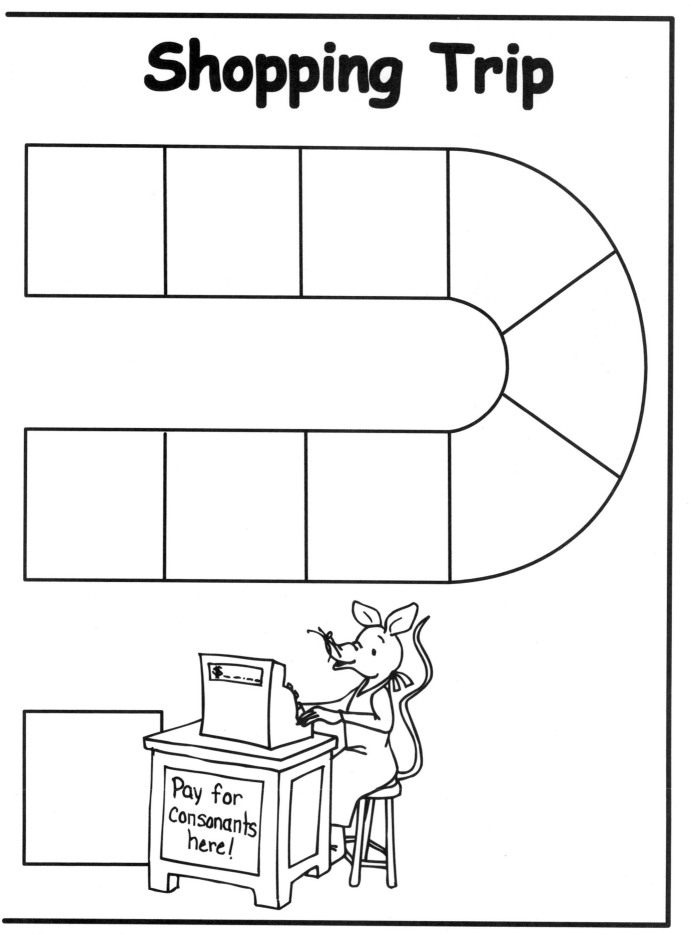

Pay for Consonants here!

Consonants © 2002 Monday Morning Books, Inc.

# Shopping Trip

Trace the letters. Name the picture. Write the letter for the last sound for each picture.

g  t  n

ha____

ba____

ma____

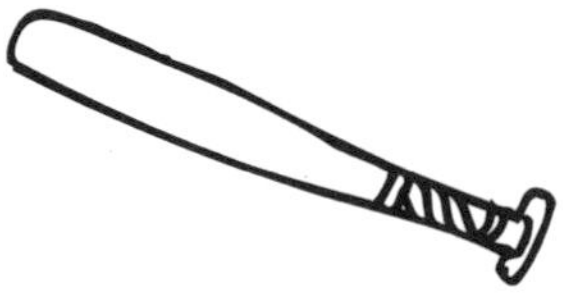

ba____

le____

pa____

Trace the letters. Name the picture. Write the letter for the last sound for each picture.

b  m  s

su ___

bu ___

ja ___

tu ___

ha ___

ga ___

Trace the letters. Name the picture. Write the letter for the last sound for each picture.

k  p  f

ca ___

el ___

ma ___

stic ___

mil ___

lea ___

Trace the letters. Name the picture. Write the letter for the last sound for each picture.

d   r   l   x

ca___     be___

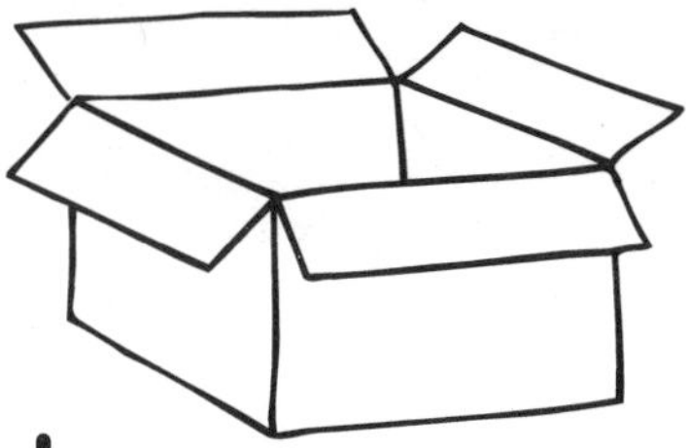

bo___     sea___

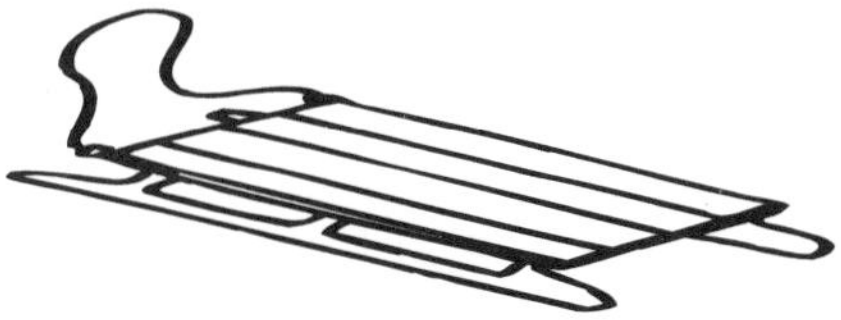

sle___     fo___

# Chicks and Eggs
## Final Consonants

**How to Play:** (For 2-3 children)

Place the consonant chick cards face down in the playing area. Place the picture egg cards face down separately from the chick cards. Each child, in turn, takes a chick card and an egg card and turns them over. If the two cards match by the final consonant sound of the picture name and the consonant letter, the player may keep the cards. If not, the cards are placed back in their same spots. Play ends when all cards are matched. Player with the most matches wins.

**How to Make:**

Duplicate the game pages. Glue onto oak tag. Color if desired. Cut the cards apart. Rubber band the chick cards and egg cards separately. Place the cards in a clasp manila envelope. Duplicate the game illustration and **How to Play** directions. Glue onto the manila envelope.

# Chicks and Eggs

# Chicks and Eggs

Name the pictures. Write the letters for the first and last sound for each picture. Use the letters on the picture.

t   r   b

___ u ___

p   c   m

___ a ___

f   w   g

___ i ___

b   x   f

___ o ___

j   r   g

___ u ___

d   s   h

___ a ___

Circle the word that matches each picture.
Write the word under the picture.

meet   man   mail

_____

paint   tent   pond

_____

bed   beet   deer

_____

seal   sand   lamp

_____

star   step   root

_____

vet   week   van

_____

Circle the word that matches each picture.
Write the word under the picture.

wet    worm    moon

_____

jam    jog    jet

_____

zip    peek    zoo

_____

boat    top    book

_____

dot    hand    heel

_____

feet    fog    flag

_____

Read the sentences under each picture. Draw a line under the sentence that tells about the picture.

The frog jumps on a log.
The frog sits on a big log.

A big bear is in the car.
A big jar is on a bear.

The goat has a vest.
The goat has a coat.

The queen has a quilt.
The queen has a quail.

Read the sentences under each picture. Draw a line under the sentence that tells about the picture.

The seal is in the tub.
The seal is in a sub.

A train is in the tent.
A tent is on the train.

Jill can jog in the park.
Jill has a job in the park.

The pan is on the moon.
The man is on the moon.

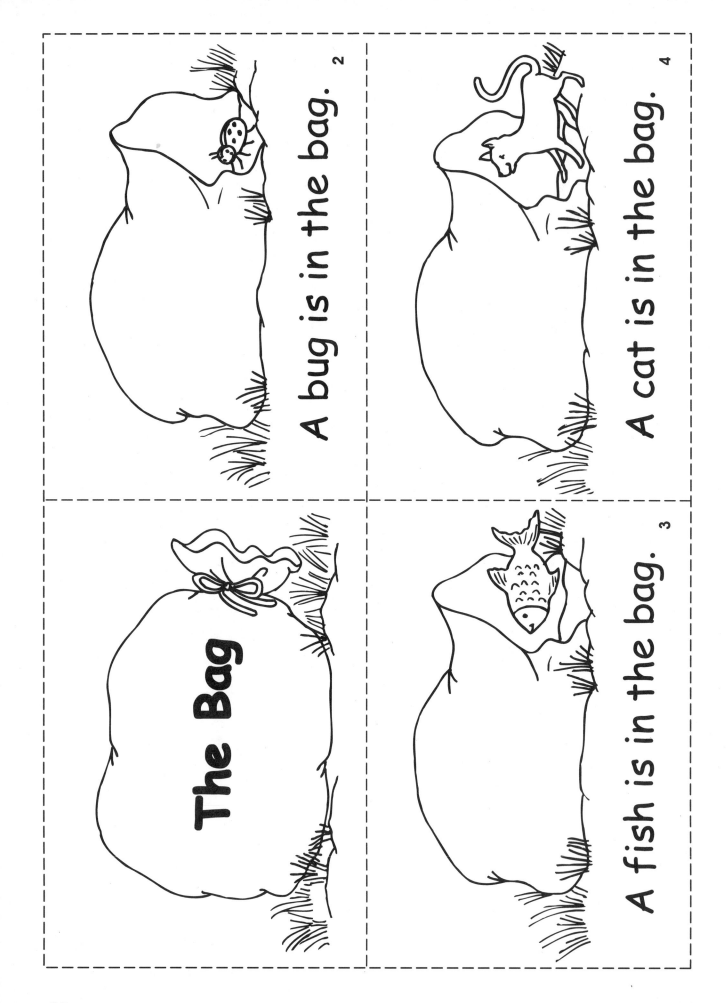

The Bag

A bug is in the bag. 2

A fish is in the bag. 3

A cat is in the bag. 4

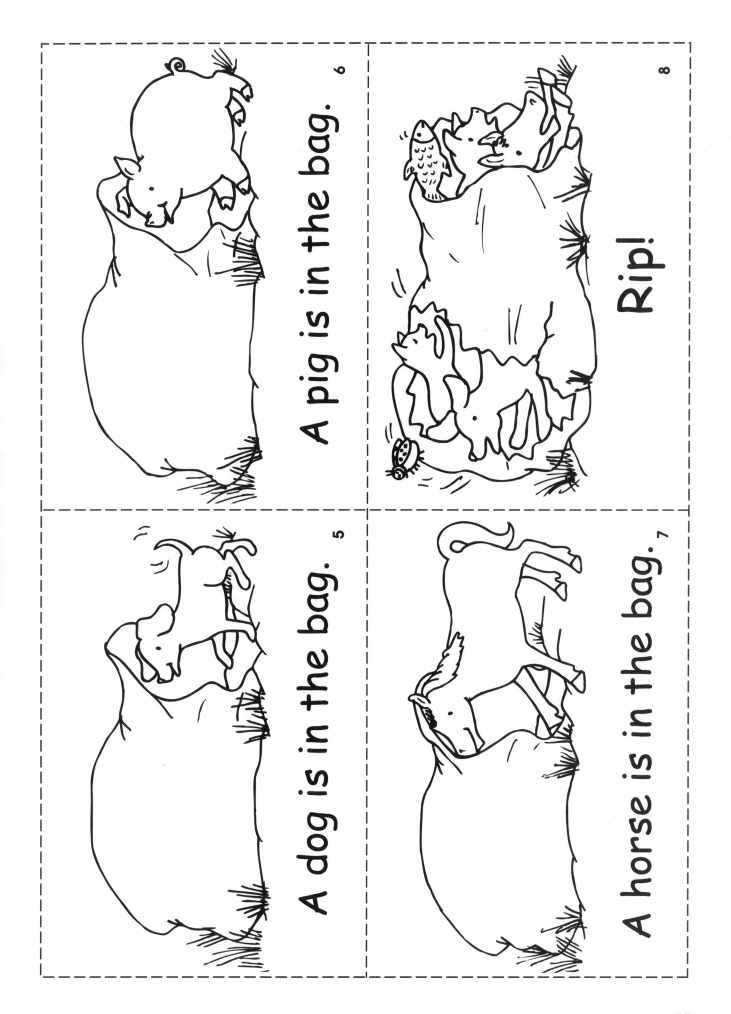

A pig is in the bag. 6

Rip! 8

A dog is in the bag. 5

A horse is in the bag. 7

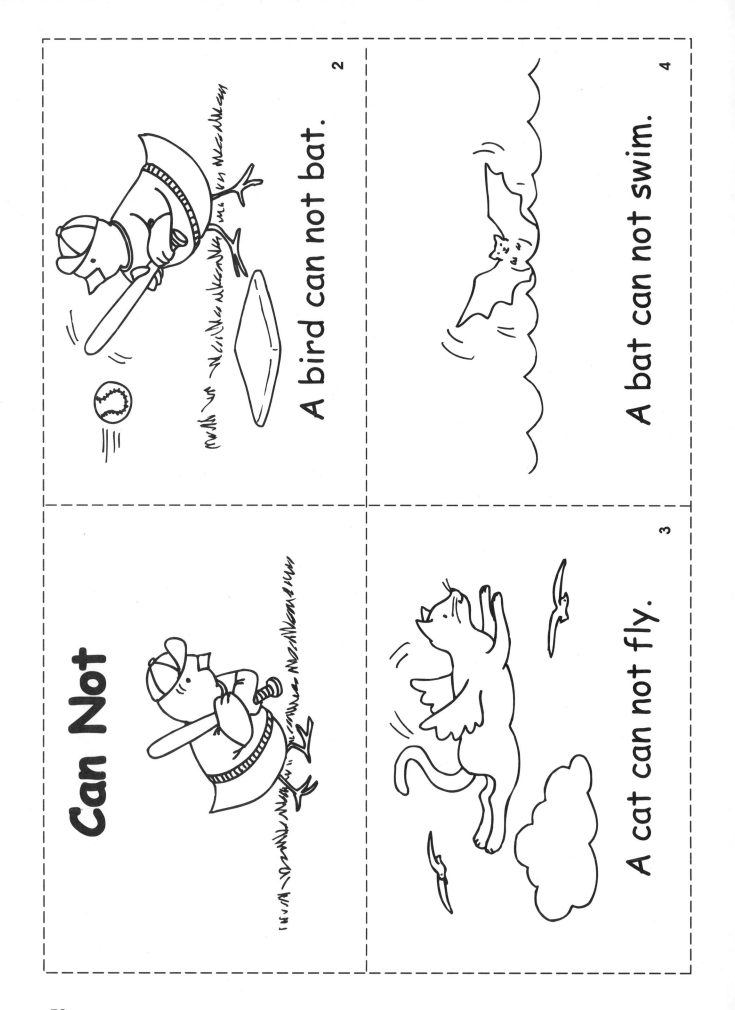

**Can Not**

A bird can not bat.

2

A cat can not fly.

3

A bat can not swim.

4

A dog can not swing.

But they can all sing!

A frog can not jog.

A little girl can not drive

Green Man

Green Man had a green farm.
The farm had a green barn. 2

Green Man had a green cow.
The cow gave green milk. 3

Green Man had a green tree.
The tree had green apples. 4

6

Green Man had a green pig.
The pig rolled in green mud.

8

A yellow duck? "Not on my
green farm," said Green Man.
"Shoo!"

5

Green Man had a green hen.
The hen gave green eggs.

7

Green Man had a green dog.
It ran after green sheep.

# Silly Duck

"Cluck, cluck," said Silly Duck. "Silly Duck," said Hen. "Ducks do not cluck. Hens do!"

2

"Woof, woof," said Silly Duck. "Silly Duck," said Dog. "Ducks do not woof. Dogs do!"

3

"Meow," said Silly Duck. "Silly Duck," said Cat. "Ducks do not meow. Cats do!"

4

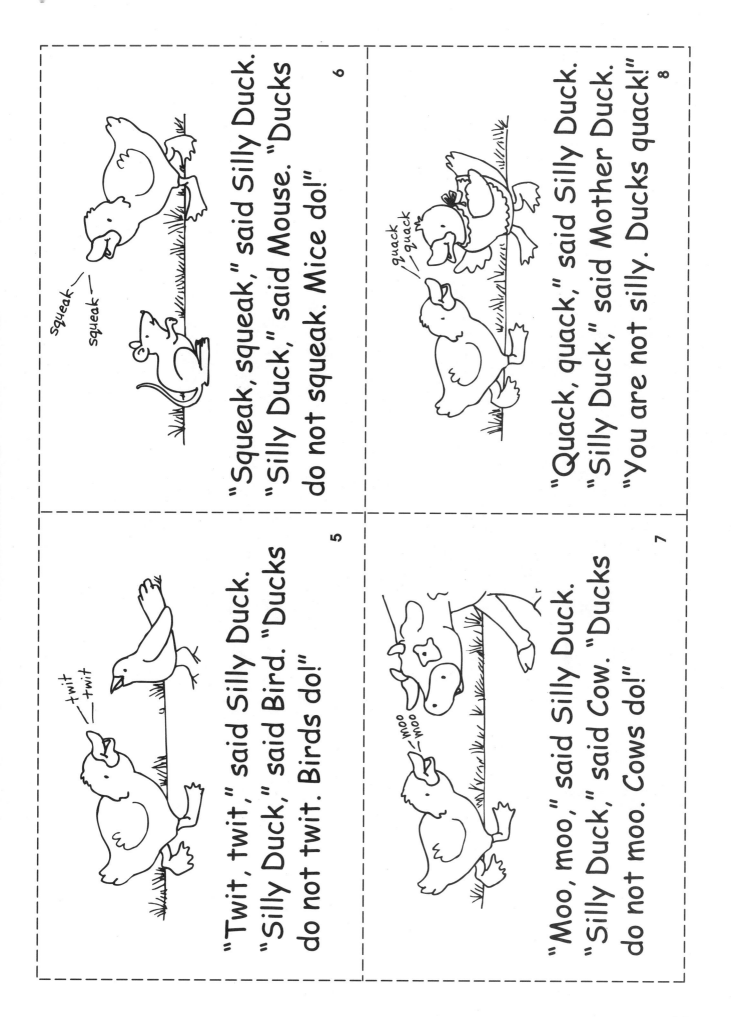

"Squeak, squeak," said Silly Duck. "Silly Duck," said Mouse. "Ducks do not squeak. Mice do!"

6

"Quack, quack," said Silly Duck. "Silly Duck," said Mother Duck. "You are not silly. Ducks quack!"

8

"Twit, twit," said Silly Duck. "Silly Duck," said Bird. "Ducks do not twit. Birds do!"

5

"Moo, moo," said Silly Duck. "Silly Duck," said Cow. "Ducks do not moo. Cows do!"

7

# The Mouse
## in the House

A mouse found a house.
But the house was too big.

2

The mouse found a house.
But the house was too small.

3

The mouse found a house.
But the house was too messy.

4

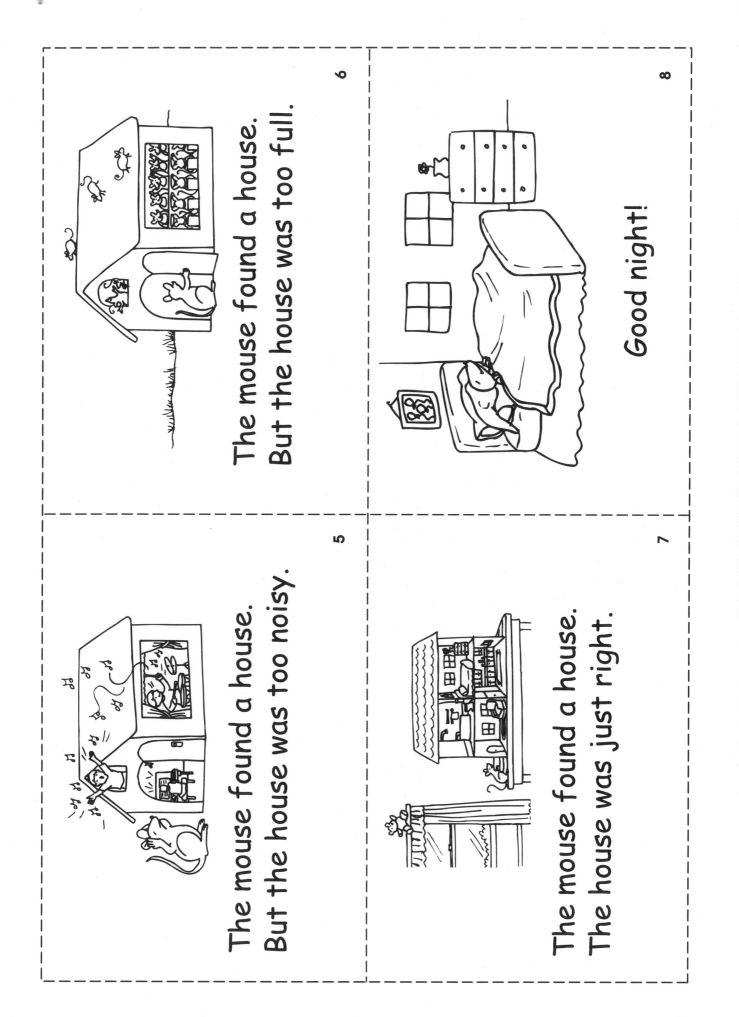

6

The mouse found a house.
But the house was too full.

8

Good night!

5

The mouse found a house.
But the house was too noisy.

7

The mouse found a house.
The house was just right.

# I know my consonant sounds!

_____
Name

Bb Cc Dd Ff Gg Hh Jj
Kk Ll Mm Nn Pp Qq Rr
Ss Tt Vv Ww Xx Yy Zz

_____
Teacher